C900701857

D0533508

GRAPHIC SCIENCE

EXPLORING

ECOSYSTEMS

with **MAX AXIOM**

SUPER SCIENTIST

Agnieszka Biskup

illustrated by Tod Smith

Raintree

www.raintreepublishers.co.uk
Visit our website to find out
more information about
Raintree books.

To order:
☎ Phone +44 (0) 1865 888066
▤ Fax +44 (0) 1865 314091
▤ Visit www.raintreepublishers.co.uk

Raintree is an imprint of Capstone Global Library Limited, a company incorporated in England and Wales
having its registered office at 7 Pilgrim Street, London EC4V 6LB
Registered company number: 6695882

Text © Capstone Press 2008
First published by Capstone Press in 2008
First published in hardback in the United Kingdom by Capstone Global Library in 2010
First published in paperback in the United Kingdom by Capstone Global Library in 2011
The moral rights of the proprietor have been asserted.

All rights reserved. No part of this publication may be reproduced in any form or by any means (including
photocopying or storing it in any medium by electronic means and whether or not transiently or incidentally
to some other use of this publication) without the written permission of the copyright owner, except in
accordance with the provisions of the Copyright, Designs and Patents Act 1988 or under the terms of a
licence issued by the Copyright Licensing Agency, Saffron House, 6--10 Kirby Street, London EC1N 8T
(www.cla.co.uk). Applications for the copyright owner's written permission should be addressed to the
publisher.

ISBN 978 1 4062 1464 2 (hardback)
14 13 12 11 10

ISBN 978 1 4062 1480 2 (paperback)
15 14 13 12 11

British Library Cataloguing in Publication Data
Biskup, Agnieszka.
Ecosystems. -- (Graphic science)
577-dc22
A full catalogue record for this book is available from the British Library.

Art Director and Designer: Bob Lentz and Thomas Emery
Cover Artist: Tod Smith
Colourist: Matt Webb
UK Editor: Harriet Milles
UK Production: Alison Parsons
Originated by Capstone Global Library
Printed and bound in China by South China Printing Company Limited

Acknowledgements
The publisher would like to thank the following for permission to reproduce copyright material:
Corel p. 17

Disclaimer
All the Internet addresses (URLs) given in this book were valid at the time of going to press. However,
due to the dynamic nature of the Internet, some addresses may have changed, or sites may have changed
or ceased to exist since publication. While the publisher regrets any inconvenience this may cause readers,
no responsibility for any such changes can be accepted by the publisher.

CONTENTS

5

Teresa's right. Every ecosystem has millions of organisms. Each is part of a species.

Members of a species are the same in many ways. They can mate and have offspring.

Chipmunks are a kind of species.

Humans are a kind of species too!

All members of a species living in the same area are known as a population.

All the chipmunks living in a forest are a population.

Ecosystems contain multiple populations of living things.

DEFINITION

nutrient substance needed by a living thing to stay healthy; plants get nutrients mainly from the soil in the form of minerals; animals get nutrients mainly from the foods they eat

Consumers that eat plants for energy are called herbivores.

This group includes tiny insects and larger animals, such as deer.

Of course, not all consumers eat plants.

Carnivores eat other animals to get energy. This group includes sharks, lions, hawks, and wolves.

Omnivores eat both plants and animals for energy.

Grizzly bears are omnivores. They eat grasses and berries, as well as salmon.

Rats, crows, and humans are omnivores too.

The sun is the main source of energy for every food chain.

Plants only change a small amount of the sun's energy into food. They use much of this energy to stay alive.

An energy pyramid tracks the path of energy through a food chain.

BOOP

BEEP

BLEE

Each level of an energy pyramid is a link in the chain.

As this pyramid will show, energy gets quickly used up in a food chain.

Only a small amount passes to other levels of consumers.

BRZZTT

PREDATOR VS. PREY

Animals that hunt other animals are called predators. Animals that are hunted are called prey.

16

Each level of consumer has even less energy available to use.

The herbivore burns most of the energy gained from the plants by breathing, walking, and reproducing.

Only a tiny portion of energy is left for the carnivore.

That's why there are far fewer carnivores at the top of the food chain than plant-eaters further down.

PYRAMID OF THE SERENGETI

ACCESS GRANTED: MAX AXIOM

Eight square kilometres in the Serengeti produces about 7,500 tons of grass. These plants can support about 350 gazelles, zebras, and wildebeest. All these animals support one lion. The population of prey and predator stays in balance with these numbers. If there were more lions in the area, they would kill too many plant-eaters and run out of food.

Not all water runs directly back into the ground.

Plants take up water through their roots.

After passing through the plant, water enters the air through tiny openings in the leaves. This process is called transpiration.

There's an oxygen cycle too.

Animals breathe out carbon dioxide, which plants take up to use in photosynthesis.

OXYGEN

CARBON DIOXIDE

Plants release oxygen in the process. Animals breathe in this oxygen, and the cycle begins again.

Rain isn't only a part of an ecosystem's water cycles, it's also a part of the climate.

Climate is the usual weather in an area over many years.

And ecosystems with similar climate, plants, and animals are called biomes.

A biome's climate often determines the kinds of living things found there.

Biomes are not specific places. A desert biome can be any desert-like ecosystem on earth, whether it's in Australia, Asia, or Africa.

KEY

DESERT	RAINFOREST
GRASSLAND	TUNDRA
DECIDUOUS FOREST	OCEAN
CONIFEROUS FOREST	

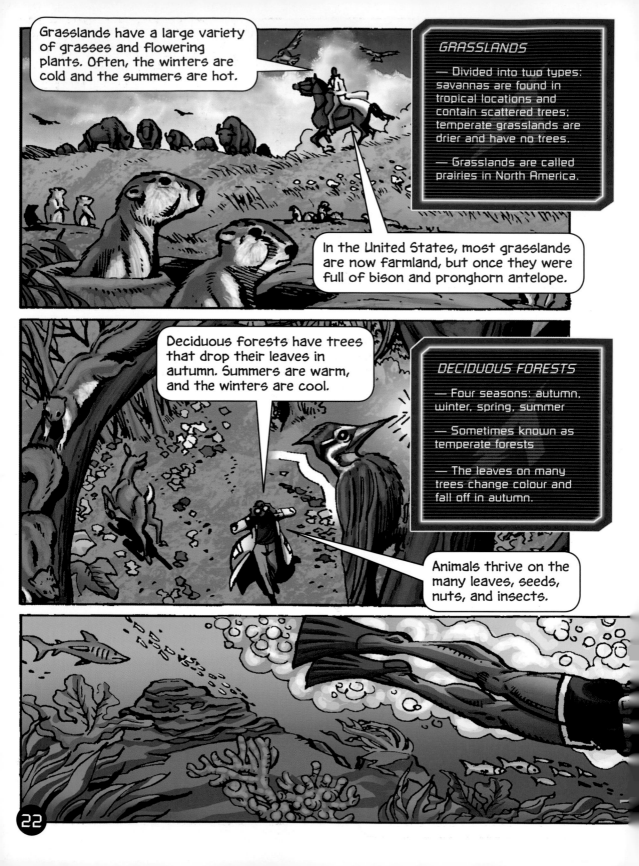

Grasslands have a large variety of grasses and flowering plants. Often, the winters are cold and the summers are hot.

GRASSLANDS

— Divided into two types: savannas are found in tropical locations and contain scattered trees; temperate grasslands are drier and have no trees.

— Grasslands are called prairies in North America.

In the United States, most grasslands are now farmland, but once they were full of bison and pronghorn antelope.

Deciduous forests have trees that drop their leaves in autumn. Summers are warm, and the winters are cool.

DECIDUOUS FORESTS

— Four seasons: autumn, winter, spring, summer

— Sometimes known as temperate forests

— The leaves on many trees change colour and fall off in autumn.

Animals thrive on the many leaves, seeds, nuts, and insects.

Long ago, mountain lions and wolves balanced deer populations. But humans eliminated many of these natural predators.

Today, deer numbers have risen in the United States. Overpopulation leads to lack of food. The hungry deer mow down plants and trees, which may never come back.

Humans also change the face of earth by cutting down forests, turning grasslands into farmland, and building on wetlands.

Unfortunately, these changes are not always for the better.

REDUCE YOUR IMPACT

You can protect the earth's ecosystems by practising conservation. Use fewer natural resources such as water and gas. Reduce waste and pollution whenever possible. Recycle bottles, cans, paper, and other recyclable materials.

MORE ABOUT ECOSYSTEMS

Ecosystems can be as large as an ocean or as small as a fishbowl. To identify the many ecosystems, some are called after their main feature, such as a pond ecosystem, a salt marsh ecosystem, or a rainforest ecosystem.

Ecosystems are fragile, and alien invasive species can be a major problem. These plants and animals have been introduced to a part of the world where they don't belong. The brown tree snake was originally from Australia and Indonesia. Somehow, this sneaky reptile slithered onto a plane and hitched a ride to the island of Guam. With few predators on Guam, the tree snake has nearly wiped out the native forest birds.

Believe it or not, the extinct passenger pigeon was once amongst the most numerous animals on earth. In the early 1800s, the passenger pigeon population was estimated at 1 to 5 billion birds. Huge migrating flocks actually darkened the sky when they passed. Largely due to over-hunting, the pigeons began to decline. By the 1890s, only small flocks were left. The last passenger pigeon died in a zoo in 1914.

In the early 1990s, scientists tried to reproduce the ecosystems of the earth inside a 1.4-hectare (3.5-acre) building called Biosphere 2 in Arizona, USA. The building contained a desert, a rainforest, and even a 4,000,000-litre (900,000-gallon) ocean. Some scientists believed buildings like Biosphere 2 could support life on the Moon or Mars. But after only two disappointing missions inside, the experiments ended.

 The rainforest is one of the largest biomes on earth. Sadly, more than 0.6 hectare (1.5 acres) of rainforest are destroyed every second.

 People should do their bit every day to protect the environment. Special days throughout the year help us to remember this important task:

Earth Day (22 April) – celebrates clean air, land, and water

World Environment Day (5 June) – encourages environmental awareness worldwide

MORE ABOUT

MAX AXIOM
SUPER SCIENTIST

Real name: Maxwell Axiom
Height: 1.86 m (6 ft 1 in.)
Weight: 87 kg (13 st. 10 lb.)
Eyes: Brown   **Hair:** None

Super capabilities: Super intelligence; able to shrink to the size of an atom; sunglasses give X-ray vision; lab coat allows for travel through time and space.

Origin: Since birth, Max Axiom seemed destined for greatness. His mother, a marine biologist, taught her son about the mysteries of the sea. His father, a nuclear physicist and volunteer park warden, showed Max the wonders of the earth and sky.

One day, while Max was hiking in the hills, a megacharged lightning bolt struck him with blinding fury. When he awoke, he discovered a new-found energy and set out to learn as much about science as possible. He travelled the globe studying every aspect of the subject. Then he was ready to share his knowledge and new identity with the world. He had become Max Axiom, Super Scientist.

GLOSSARY

carbon dioxide colourless, odourless gas that people and animals breathe out

community populations of people, plants, or animals that live together in the same area and depend on each other

ecology study of the relationships between plants and animals in their environments

environment the natural world of the land, water, and air

mate to join together for breeding

offspring animals born to a set of parents

organism living plant or animal

population group of people, animals, or plants living in a certain place

recycle process of turning something old into something new

transpiration process by which plants give off moisture into the atmosphere

FIND OUT MORE

Books

100 Facts on Rainforests, Camilla de la Bedoyere (Miles Kelly Publishing, 2008)

Carbon-Oxygen and Nitrogen Cycles (Earth's Processes series), Rebecca Harman (Heinemann Library, 2005)

Changing Ecosystems, Michael Bright (Heinemann Library, 2009)

Predicting the Effects of Climate Change, John Townsend (Heinemann Library, 2009)

The War in Your Backyard: Life in an Ecosystem, Louise and Richard Spilsbury (Raintree, 2006)

Websites

www.wwf.org.uk
Visit the World Wild Fund for Nature's website to find out what steps are being taken to protect endangered species and their habitats.

www.envirolink.org
The website provides up-to-date news and information on the environment.

INDEX